MW00944376

Alphabestiary

26 Poems and Drawings
for Easily Alarmed Children and
the Adults Who Like to Alarm Them

Ian McDowell

For Sara Frances Barnes McDowell, who introduced me to Charles Addams and Maurice Sendak, but died before we could have shared the work of Edward Gorey.

The giant **Axolotl** is unfond
of those who frolic in his placid pond.
Should splashing children waken him,
he'll drag them deep and feast on them.

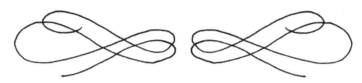

The **Blooderfly** is very sly

as she flits through the Summer air.

She looks harmless and so pretty,

but of her sharp tongue you best beware!

For the Blooderfly will drain you dry

and leave your husk all hollow there.

So, when in the sunlit meadow,

dear children, please take care!

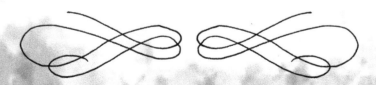

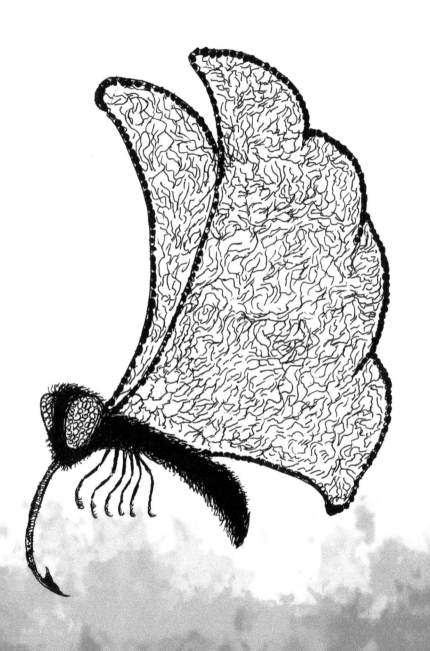

The **Creeper** comes a-creeping
down your midnight hall.
You lie abed unsleeping
but don't hear him at all.
Perhaps he means no malice;
Perhaps it's all a lark.
But maybe you should ask him
why he's so silent in the dark.

The **Deaddy Bear**

is less than nice.

You will not try

to hug him twice!

The **Earwig** is a naughty bug
who crawls, while you lie sleeping,
into your ear, my dearest dear,
where he'll cause you so much weeping.
I'll bring you tea and biscuits
to distract you from your pain,
but that's all that I can do for you
while he feasts upon your brain.

The **Frog King** comes a hunting
from his dismal swamp.
He scorns bugs and flies;
it's on your plump thighs
that he wants to chomp.

My dear, there's nothing I can do
to save you from the **Ghastly-Grue.**
Very soon, he'll come for you,
so I guess I best bid you adieu.

The **Hellgramite** lurks beneath
the inviting playground sand.
If you scoop with spade and bucket,
it will seize your digging hand.
Before you can squeak a syllable,
it will drag you down below.
And what will happen underground?
You don't want to know!

The **Iguanodon** did not eat meat?
My dears, that isn't true!
Nor is the scaly beast extinct.
See? Here he comes for you!
Best take flight, my darling dears
or be hoist high on spiky thumbs.
This fellow likes plump children
even more than you like plums!

The **Jub-Jub Bird** makes its nest
from the hair of little girls.
Whether straight and black as night
or in waves of golden curls.
That is why, my lovely,
I must clip you bald,
even though the prospect
leaves you quite appalled.
Don't struggle, dearest darling,
do not wail and shriek!
Better your hair is shorn by clippers,
than torn out by a beak!

Of the horned and hairy **Krampus**,
not much can be said,
except he comes at Christmastide
to make wicked children dead.
In the cold hollow of December
you should lie abed at night
and reflect upon the wrong you've done
and how to make it right.

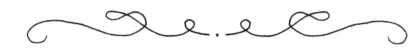

The Long-Legged **Beastie**'s
lurching stride
cannot be outrun.
Take care you don't
end up inside
the Beastie, little one.

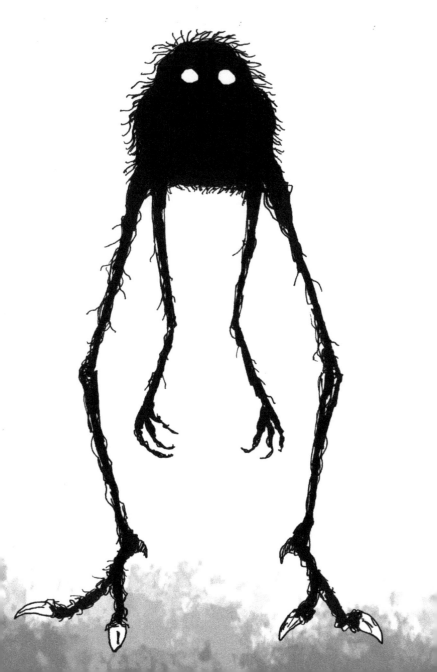

The **Mome-Rath** looks quite comical.

It's an absurd ungainly beast.

But its rage is astronomical,

so, don't annoy it in the least.

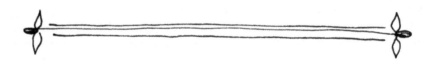

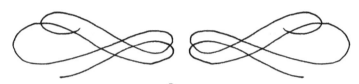

The **Nostferatu** sleeps
the day away
in his cozy crypt
amongst the dead,
but nightly drains your life away
sipping you like a tea cup
in your bed.

The **Ogress** is a horrid hag,
who'll pop you in her child-skin bag
and drag you to her witch's cave;
stew-of-you is what she craves.

The **Pugglewump** is on the prowl,
but you won't hear it howl or growl.
It creeps silent on the ground,
stalking you without a sound.

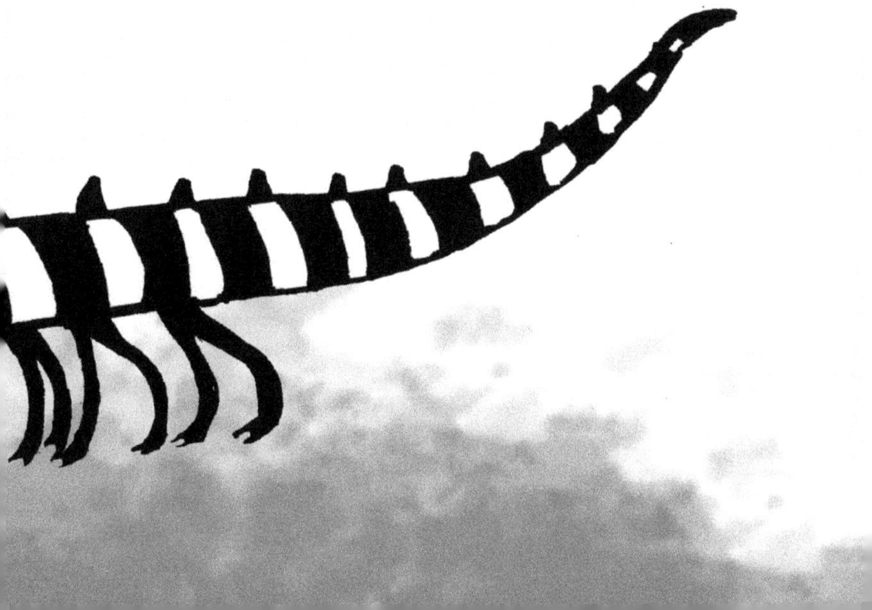

The **Quetzalcoatl** is a flying snake,
so, watch the sky, for goodness sake!
You must take care, my little dove,
lest you be strangled from above!

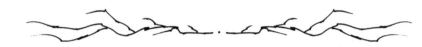

The **Rawrzer**'s breath is frightful,
due to his large and rotting teeth.
As a guest he's not delightful,
but a cause for fear and grief.

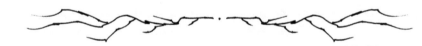

Don't go hunting for the **Snark**
after nightfall in the park.
Don't seek him in the sunlit lane.
Don't seek him in the pouring rain.
Of the Snark, keep this in mind;
he's not someone you want to find!

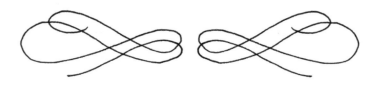

The **Terror-Fairy** is so tiny
but has a wicked sting.
Don't you dare provoke her;
she's a deadly little thing.

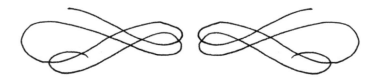

The **Undertoad** is lurking
just past the pebbled beach,
waiting for your wading
to bring you in his reach.

Caught fast in his clammy grasp,
you'll drown in his abode.
And that is why you must, my dears,
beware the Undertoad!

The **Velociphant** is very large
and oh, so awfully fast.
The day you end up in its way
may prove to be your last.
One instant, it's in Delhi,
The next, it is in Rome,
then the beast has trampled you
in the garden of your home!

The **Werewolf**'s only beastly
when influenced by the moon,
and doesn't seem so fiendish
at tea-time or at noon.
It might be the vicar or your nanny,
the postman or your nurse,
or dear Mother turned blood-thirsty
by her hairy lunar curse.

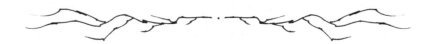

The **Xolotl** has a chihuahua's head
and backwards-facing feet.
He's yet another character
you never want to meet!

The **Yeti** is abominable,
which means he's far from nice.
He doesn't like intruders
in his realm of snow and ice.
Avoid the frozen mountain
and the snow-crowned hill,
lest this man-beast come a-roaring
with no thought but "Kill!"

The **Zugg** is rather like a slug,
all gelatinous and slimy!
But it's bigger and will swallow you
before the gardener can shout
"blimey!"

CPSIA information can be obtained
at www.ICGtesting.com
Printed in the USA
BVHW091930040320
574104BV00008B/340